MUSIC FROM THE MOVIES

THE BIG SCREEN COLLECTION

SECTION 1 THE ACTION COLLECTION

SECTION 2 THE FILM NOIR COLLECTION

SECTION 3 THE CLASSIC FILM COLLECTION

WISE PUBLICATIONS
PART OF THE MUSIC SALES GROUP
LONDON / NEW YORK / PARIS / SYDNEY / COPENHAGEN / BERLIN / MADRID / TOKYO

Published by

WISE PUBLICATIONS
14-15 Berners Street, London W1T 3LJ, UK

Exclusive Distributors:

MUSIC SALES LIMITED
Distribution Centre, Newmarket Road,
Bury St Edmunds, Suffolk IP33 3YB, UK

MUSIC SALES PTY LIMITED
20 Resolution Drive,
Caringbah, NSW 2229, Australia

Order No. AM1002474
ISBN 978-1-84938-920-4
This book © Copyright 2010 Wise Publications,
a division of Music Sales Limited.

Music processed by Paul Ewers Music Design.
Section 1: new music arrangements by Jack Long.
Section 2: music arranged by Derek Jones.
Cover designed by Liz Barrand.

Previously published as:
Music From The Movies: The Action Collection,
Music From The Movies: The Film Noir Collection,
Big Screen Themes.

Printed in the EU

www.musicsales.com

SECTION 1

THE ACTION

COLLECTION

Air Force One
(Welcome Aboard, Sir)

Composed by Jerry Goldsmith

7

Armageddon
(Theme)

Composed by Trevor Rabin

Moderately

Backdraft
(Show Me Your Firetruck)

Composed by Hans Zimmer

The Bourne Identity/
The Bourne Supremacy
(Main Titles/Atonement)

Composed by John Powell

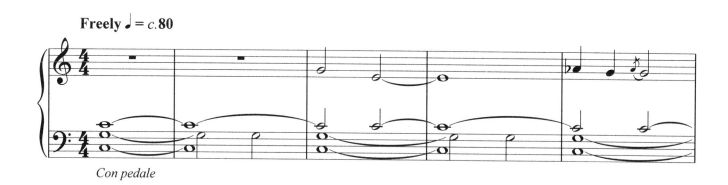

Crouching Tiger, Hidden Dragon
(Eternal Vow)

Composed by Tan Dun

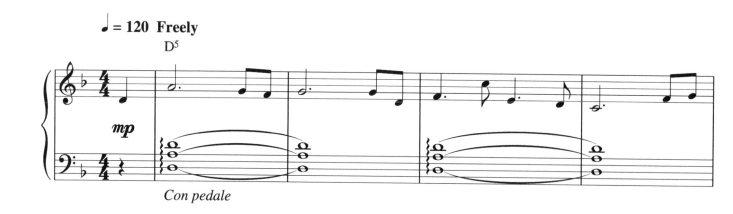

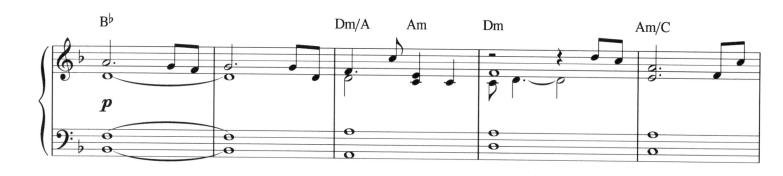

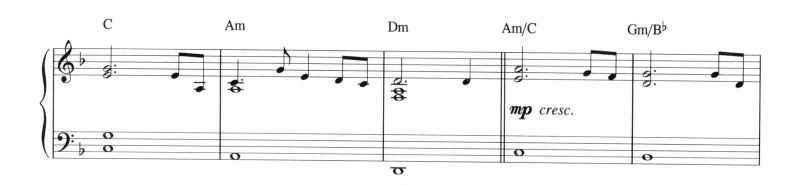

Die Hard
(Tagaki Dies)

Composed by Michael Kamen

Face/Off
(Ready For The Big Ride, Bubba)

Composed by John Powell

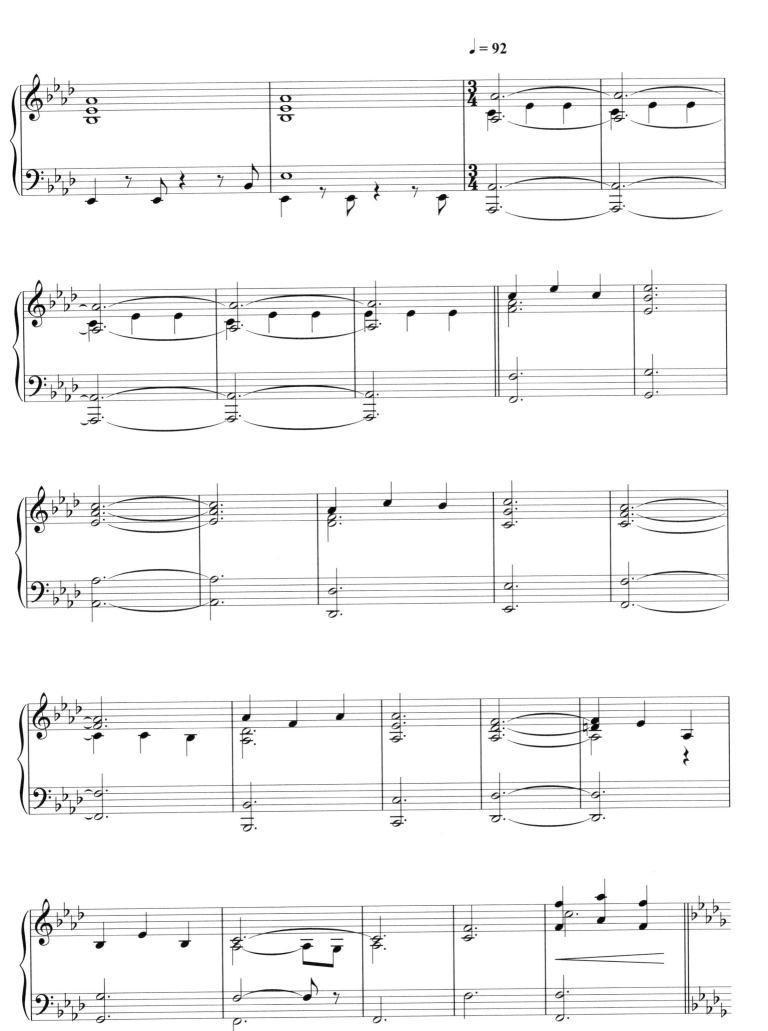

28

29

First Blood
(It's A Long Road)

Composed by Jerry Goldsmith

Con Air
(Lear Crash)

Composed by Trevor Rabin & Mark Mancina

A Fistful Of Dollars
(Title Theme)

Composed by Ennio Morricone

loco

To Coda ⊕

D.%. al Coda

loco

✛ **Coda**

Gladiator
(Now We Are Free)

Composed by Hans Zimmer, Lisa Gerrard & Klaus Badelt

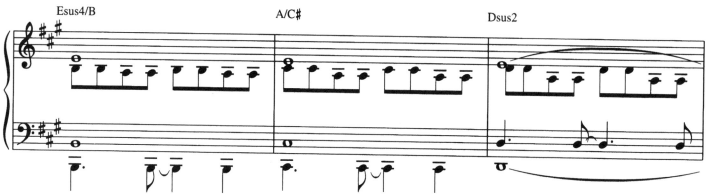

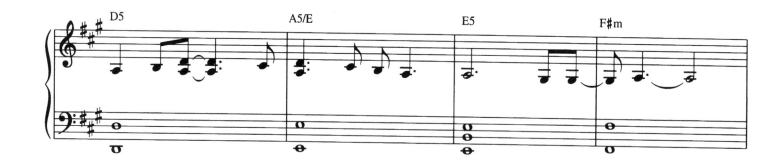

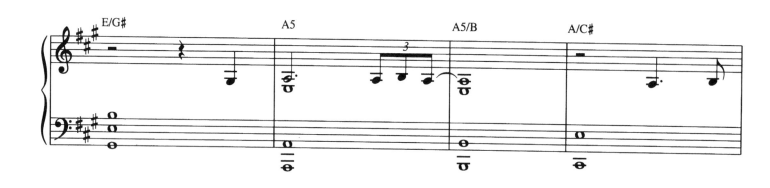

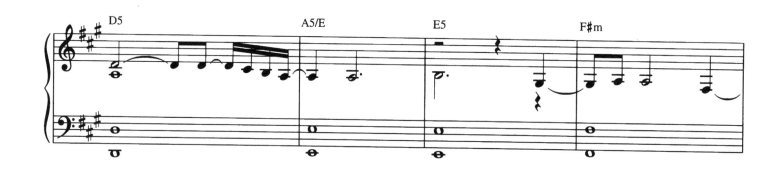

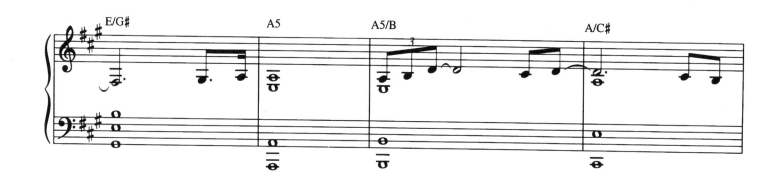

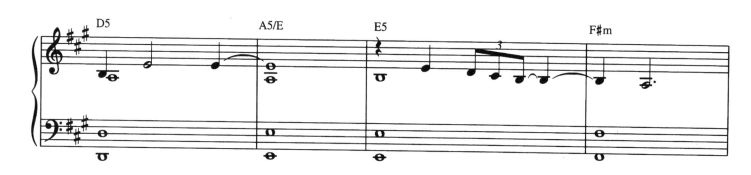

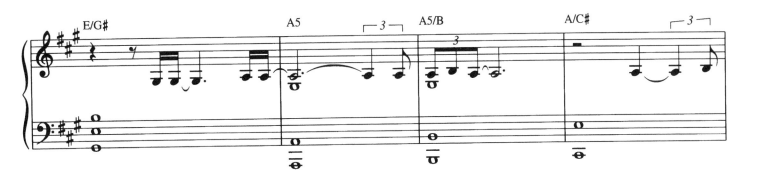

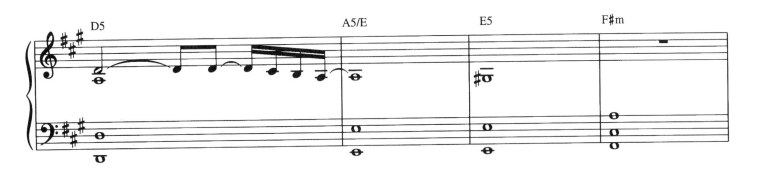

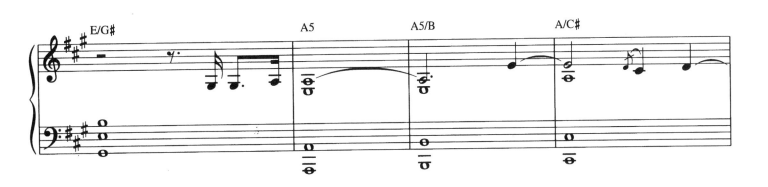

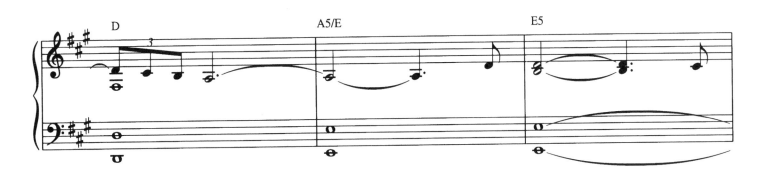

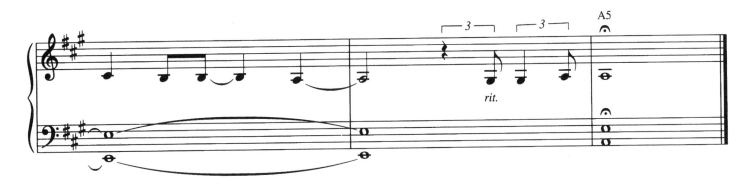

Goldfinger
(Title Theme)

Composed by John Barry

The Italian Job
(It's Caper Time: Self Preservation Society)

Composed by Quincy Jones

55

Play 3 times

Kung Fu Hustle
(Fisherman's Song Of The East China Sea)

Composed by Ma Sheng Long & Gu Guan Ren

Play 3 times

Live And Let Die
(Title Theme)

Composed by Linda McCartney & Paul McCartney

tempo primo (♩ = ♪)

Mission: Impossible
(Title Theme/Love Theme)

Composed by Lalo Schifrin/Danny Elfman

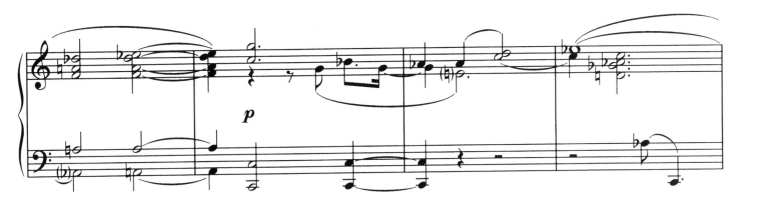

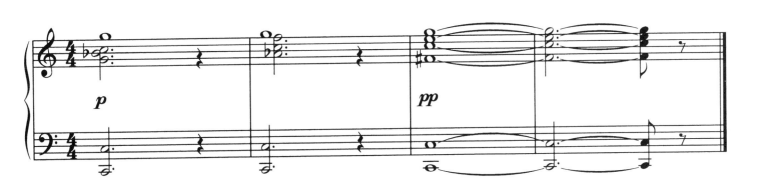

The Rock
(Theme)

Composed by Nicholas Glennie Smith & Hans Zimmer

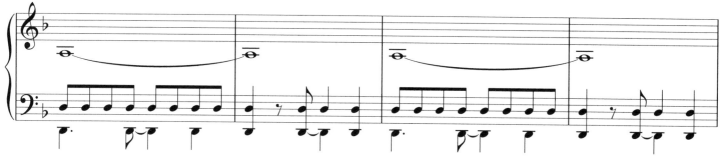

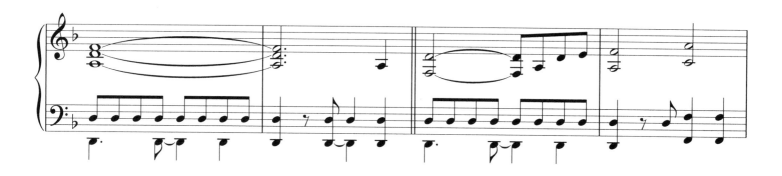

Speed
(Main Title/End Title)

Composed by Mark Mancina

Mr. & Mrs. Smith

(Assassin's Tango)

Composed by John Powell

84

Tomorrow Never Dies
(Surrender)

Composed by David Arnold

True Lies
(Main Titles/End Credits)

Composed by Carlos Gardel & Brad Fiedel

90

D.S. al Fine

Top Gun
(Anthem)

Composed by Harold Faltermeyer

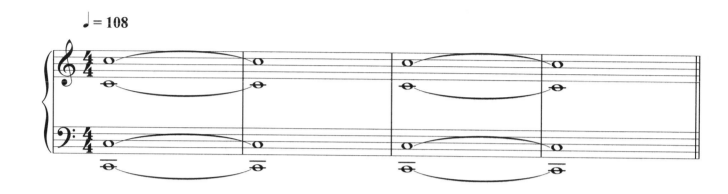

SECTION 2 THE FILM NOIR COLLECTION

Blue Velvet
(Mysteries Of Love)
Composed by Angelo Badalamenti

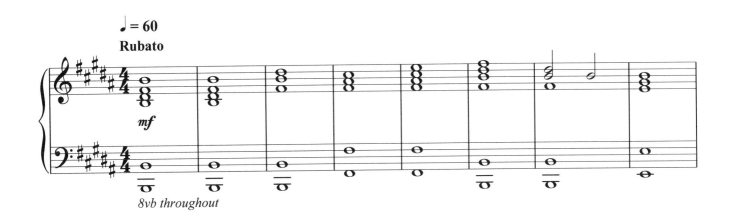

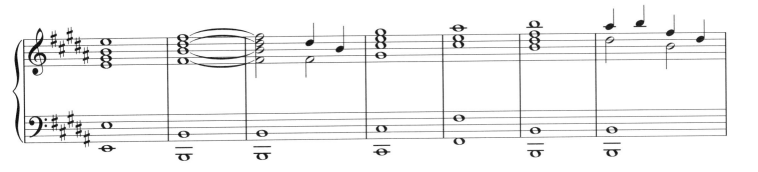

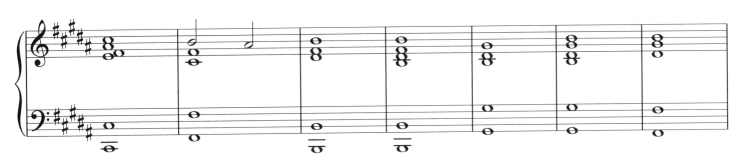

Angel Heart
(Looking For Johnny/Johnny Favourite)

Composed by Trevor Jones

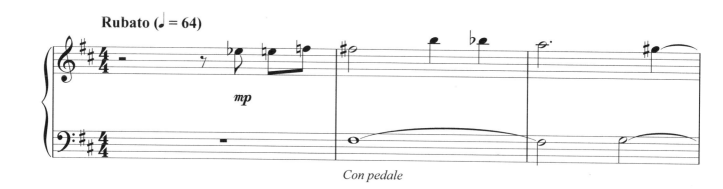

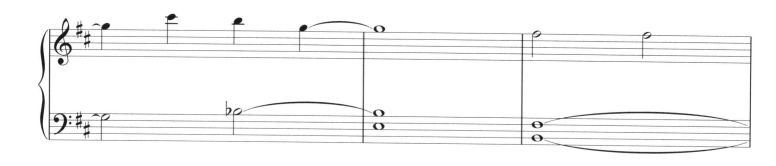

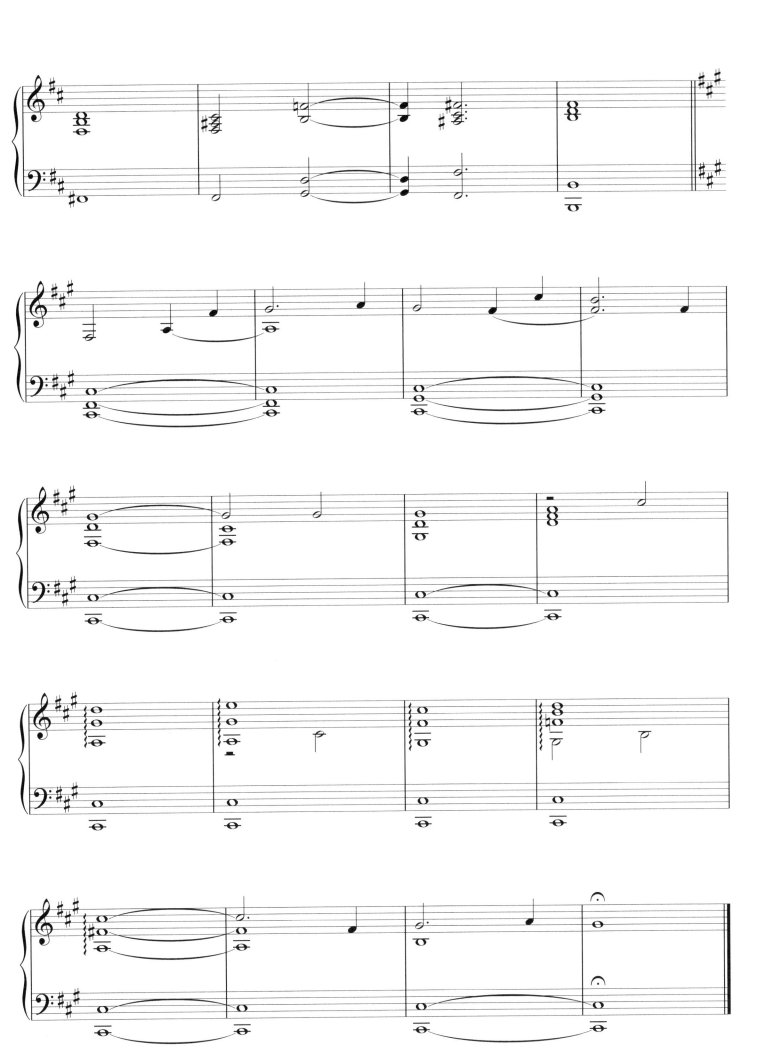

The Big Sleep
(End Credits)

Composed by Jerry Fielding

Blood Simple
(Blood Simple)

Composed by Carter Burwell

♩ = 100

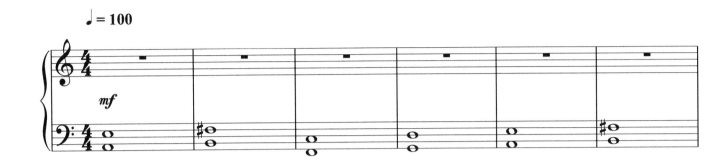

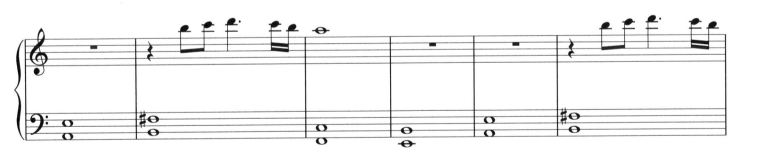

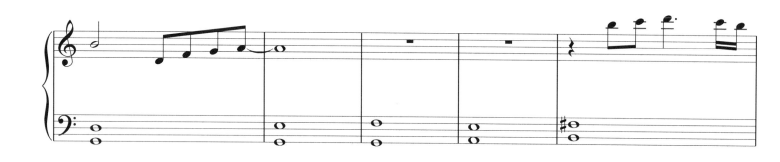

Repeat to fade

13

Cape Fear
(Prelude)

Composed by Bernard Herrmann

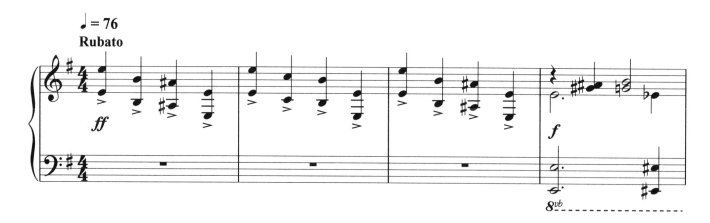

15

Chinatown
(Love Theme/Jake And Evelyn)

Composed by Jerry Goldsmith

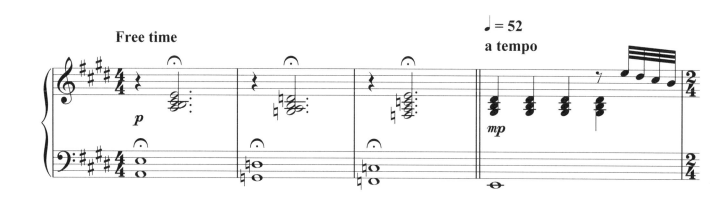

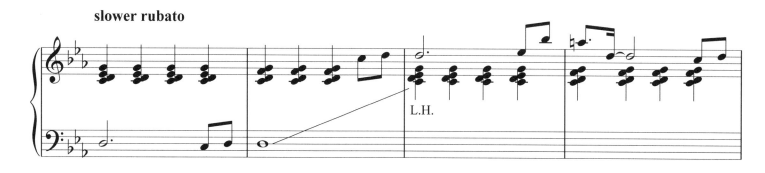

free time

17

Farewell, My Lovely
(Marlowe's Theme)

Composed by David Shire

20

21

Dead Men Don't Wear Plaid
(End Credits)

Composed by Miklós Rózsa

24

25

Double Indemnity
(Mrs. Dietrichson/The Conspiracy)

Composed by Miklós Rózsa

Dressed To Kill
(The Shower)

Composed by Pino Donaggio

Force Of Evil
(Main Title Theme)

Composed by David Raksin

Gilda
(Main Title Theme)

Composed by Hugo Friedhofer

In A Lonely Place
(Main Title Theme)

Composed by George Antheil

Le Jeu De La Vérité
(Blues For Guylaine)

Composed by André Hossein

41

Insomnia
(Closing Titles)

Composed by David Julyan

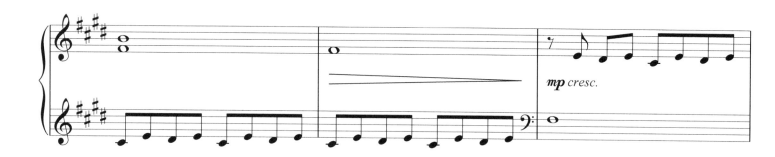

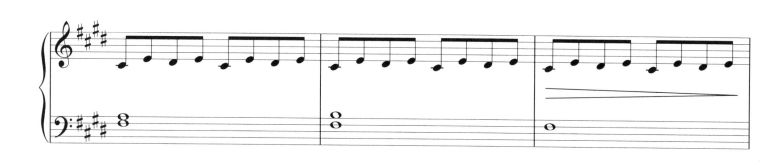

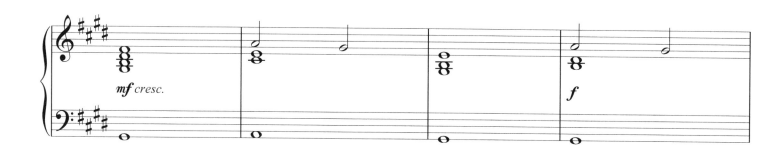

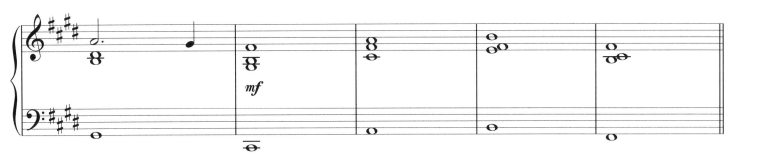

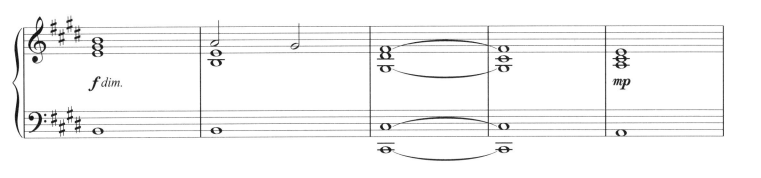

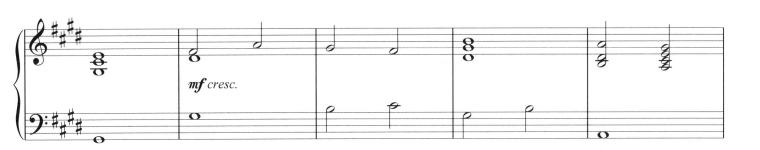

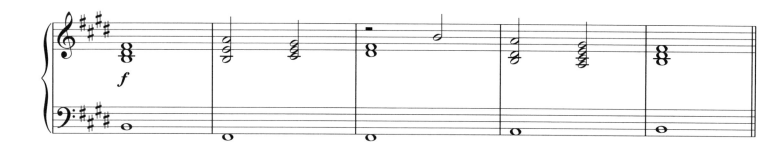

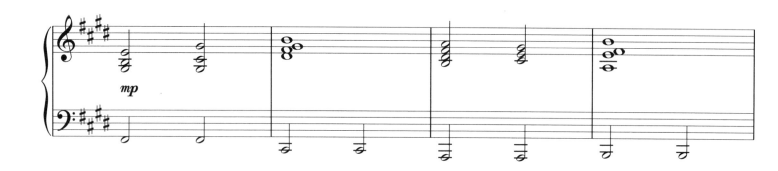

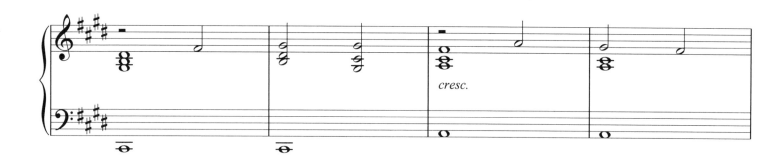

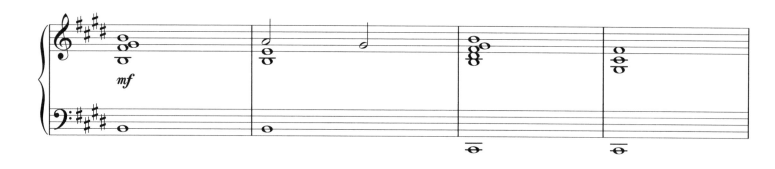

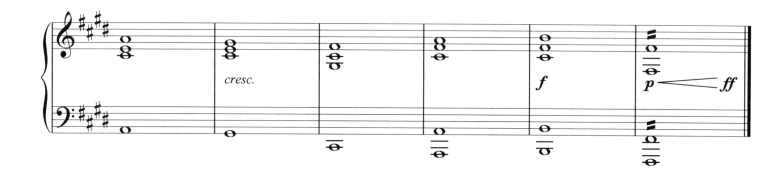

L.A. Confidential
(The Victor)

Composed by Jerry Goldsmith

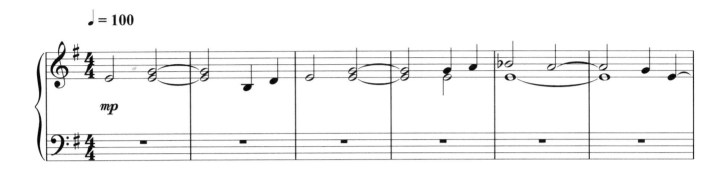

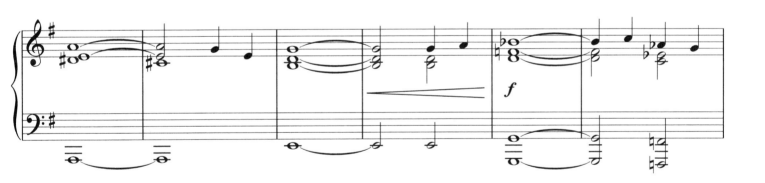

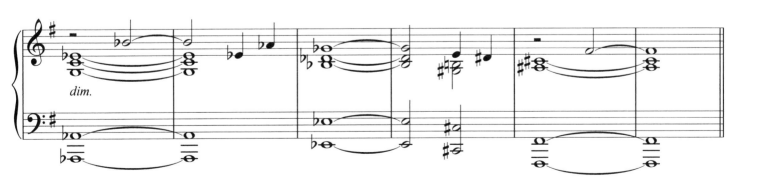

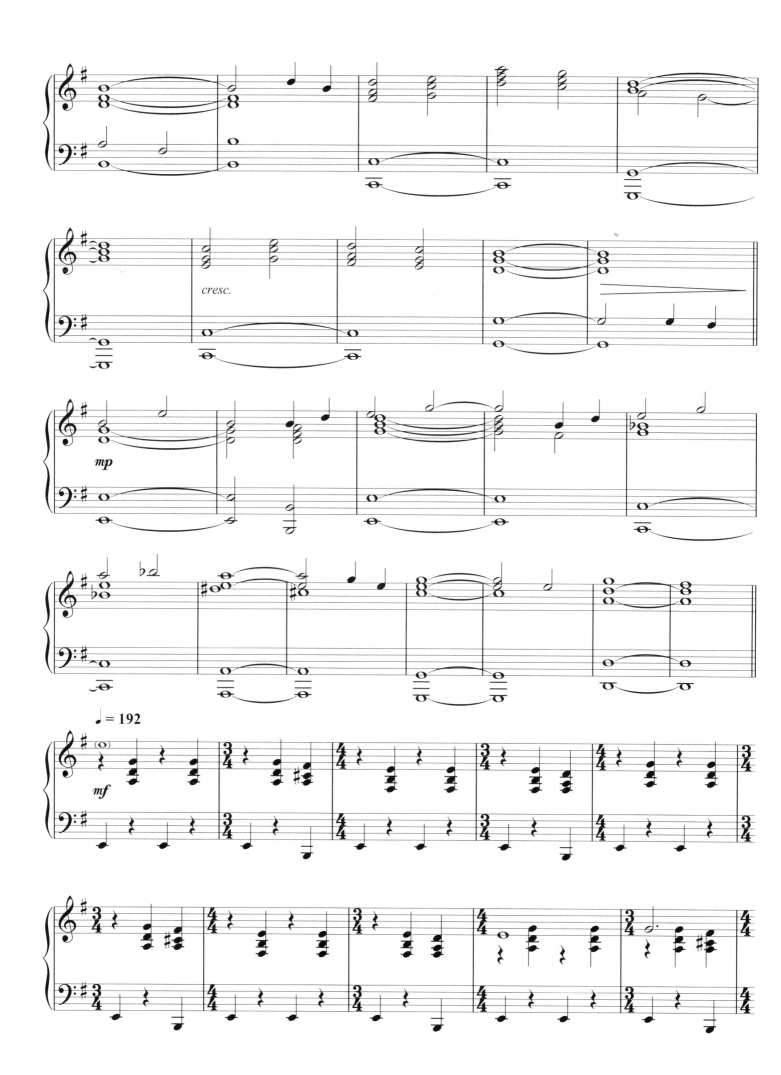

The Lady From Shanghai
(Main Title Theme)

Composed by Heinz Roemheld

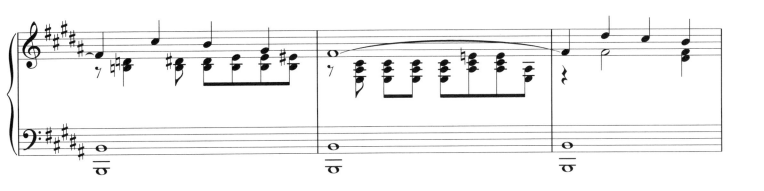

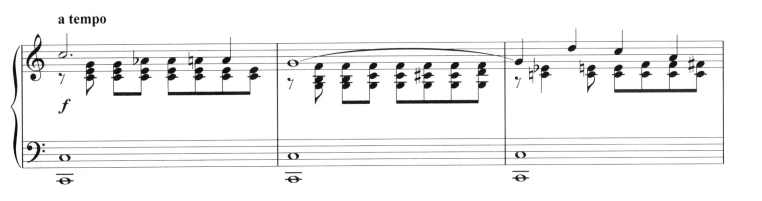

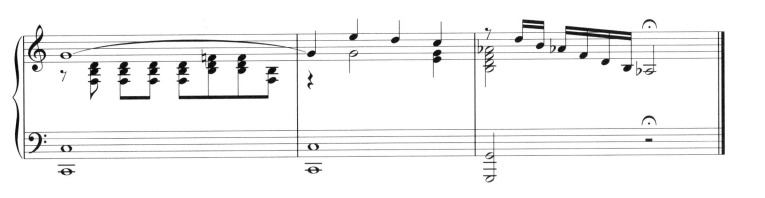

The Last Seduction
(Main Theme/Trish)

Composed by Joseph Vitarelli

53

55

56

Repeat to fade

57

The Man Who Wasn't There
(The Trial Of Ed Crane)

Composed by Carter Burwell

Mulholland Dr.
(Mulholland Drive/Love Theme)

Composed by Angelo Badalamenti

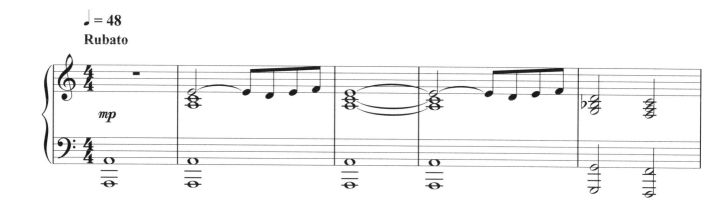

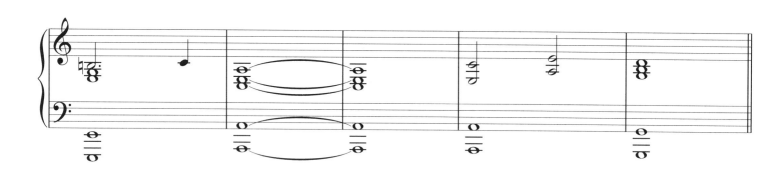

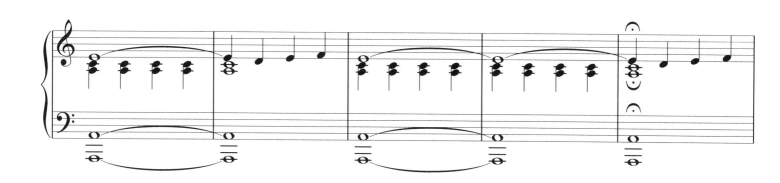

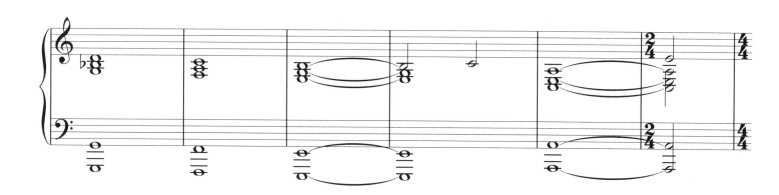

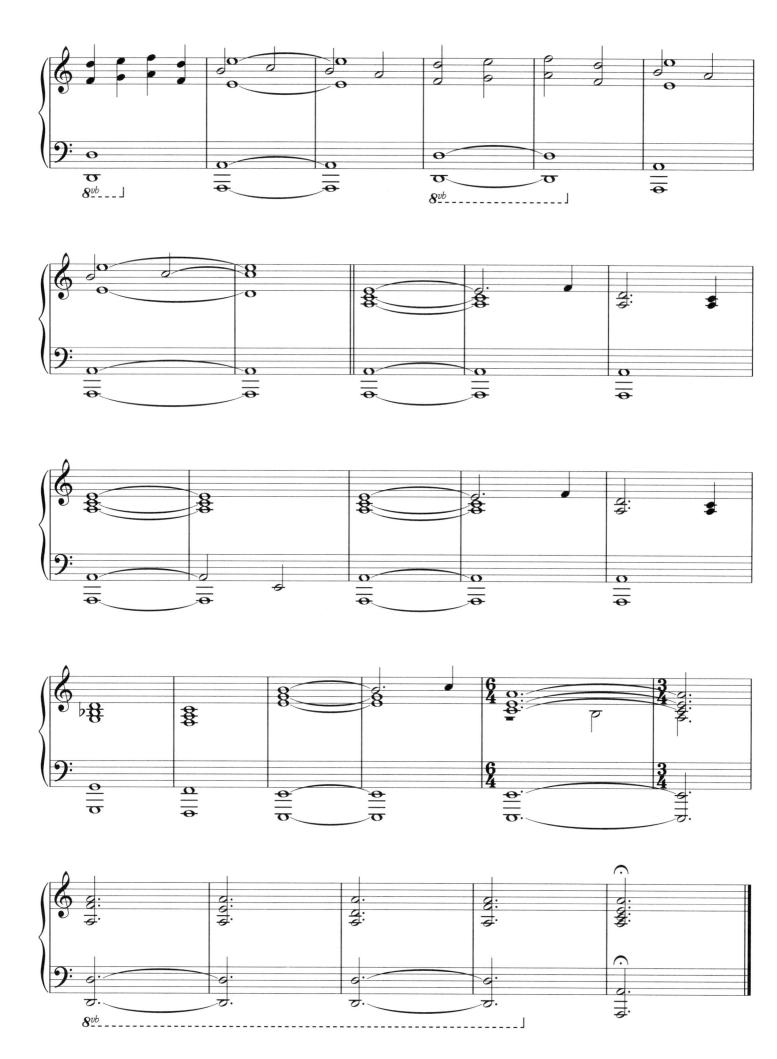

Rebecca
(Main Theme/Hotel Lobby)

Composed by Franz Waxman

64

Sea Of Love
(Fear And Passion)

Composed by Trevor Jones

Repeat ad lib. to fade

71

Sunset Boulevard
(Prelude/Sunset Boulevard Cast)

Composed by Franz Waxman

Con pedale

morendo

f

dim.

Grandioso ♩ = 104

cresc.

rit.

ff

73

Sin City
(The Big Fat Kill)

Composed by John Debney

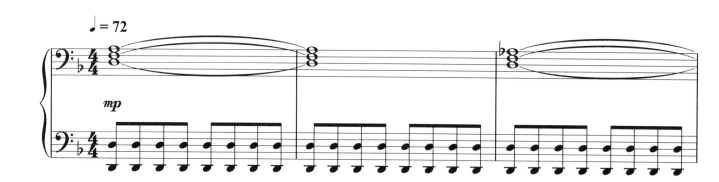

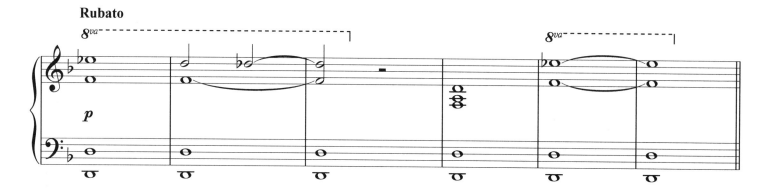

75

Sweet Smell Of Success
(Main Title Theme)

Composed by Elmer Bernstein

81

The Usual Suspects
(Main Theme)

Composed by John Ottman

D.S. al Coda

Touch Of Evil
(Main Title Theme)

Composed by Henry Mancini

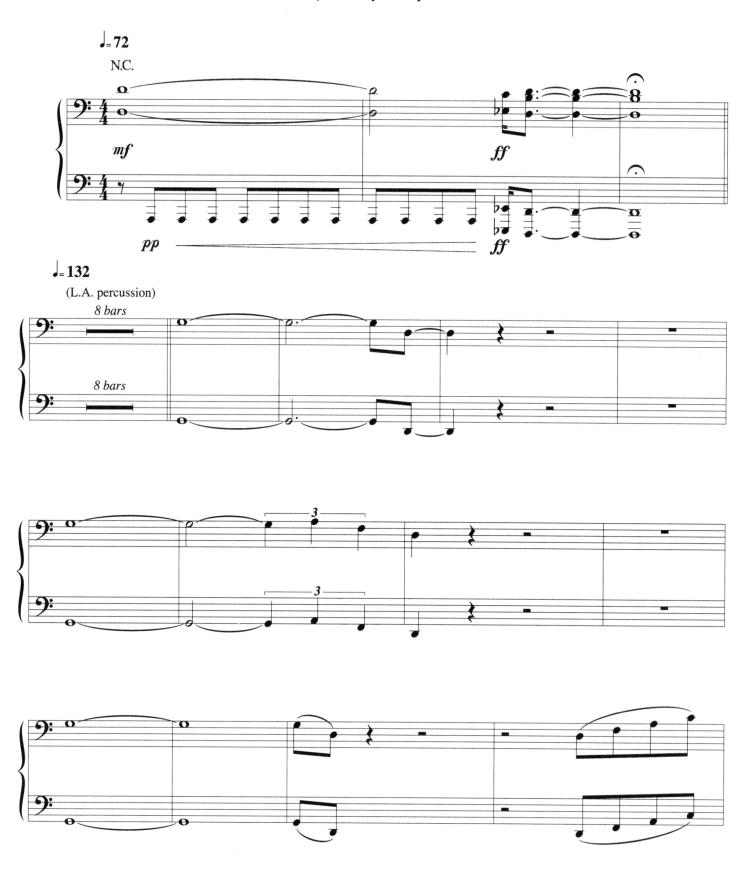

88

SECTION 3   THE CLASSIC FILM   COLLECTION

ANDANTE/REFLECTION (END TITLE)
(FROM 'WALTZ WITH BASHIR')
MUSIC BY MAX RICHTER

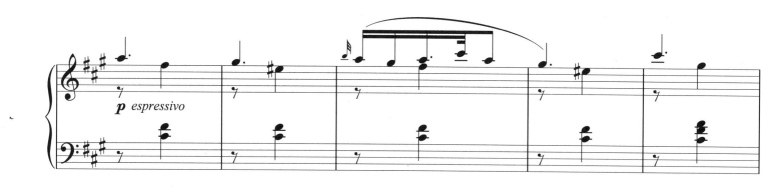

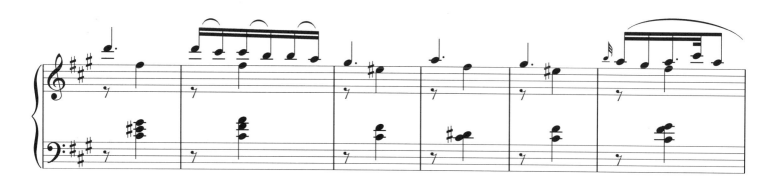

5

Benjamin And Daisy
(FROM 'THE CURIOUS CASE OF BENJAMIN BUTTON')
MUSIC BY ALEXANDRE DESPLAT

D.S. al Coda   ⊕ **Coda**

rit.

9

Dawn/Going To School
(From 'Genova')

Music by Melissa Parmenter

DAWN

Moderato ♩ = 115

11

GOING TO SCHOOL

DEATH AND TRANSFIGURATION
(FROM 'HANCOCK')
MUSIC BY JOHN POWELL

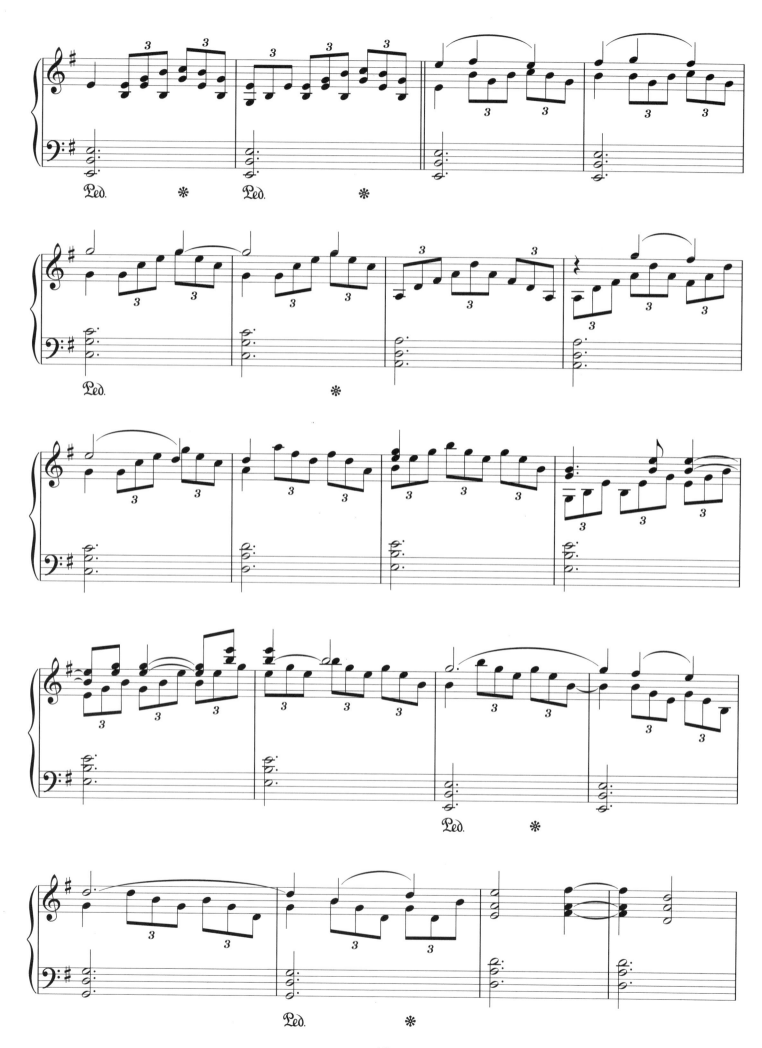

18

19

a tempo

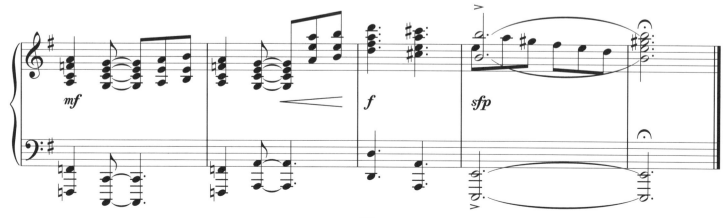

The Egg/Cycling Holiday
(FROM 'THE READER')
MUSIC BY NICO MUHLY

DMI Thing In Which New Information Is Introduced/Piano One

(FROM 'SYNECDOCHE, NEW YORK')

MUSIC BY JON BRION

Eli's Theme
(FROM 'LET THE RIGHT ONE IN')
MUSIC BY JOHAN SÖDERQVIST

THE INTERNATIONAL (END TITLE)
(FROM 'THE INTERNATIONAL')
MUSIC BY MATTHEW BELLAMY, TOM TYKWER,
JOHNNY KLIMEK & REINHOLD HEIL

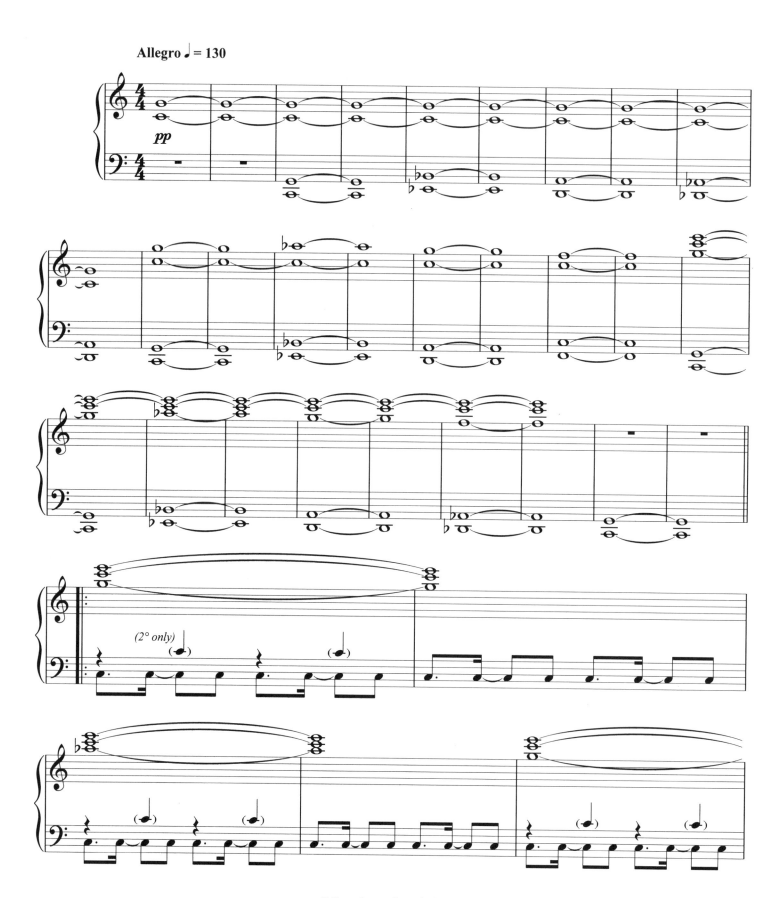

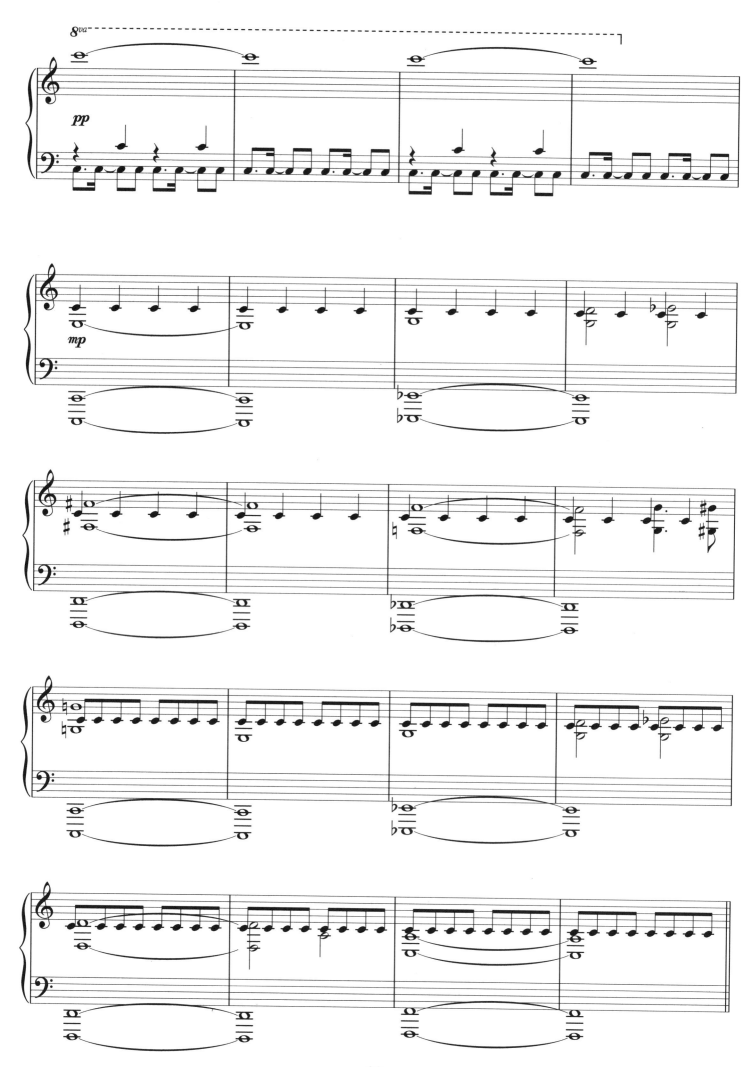

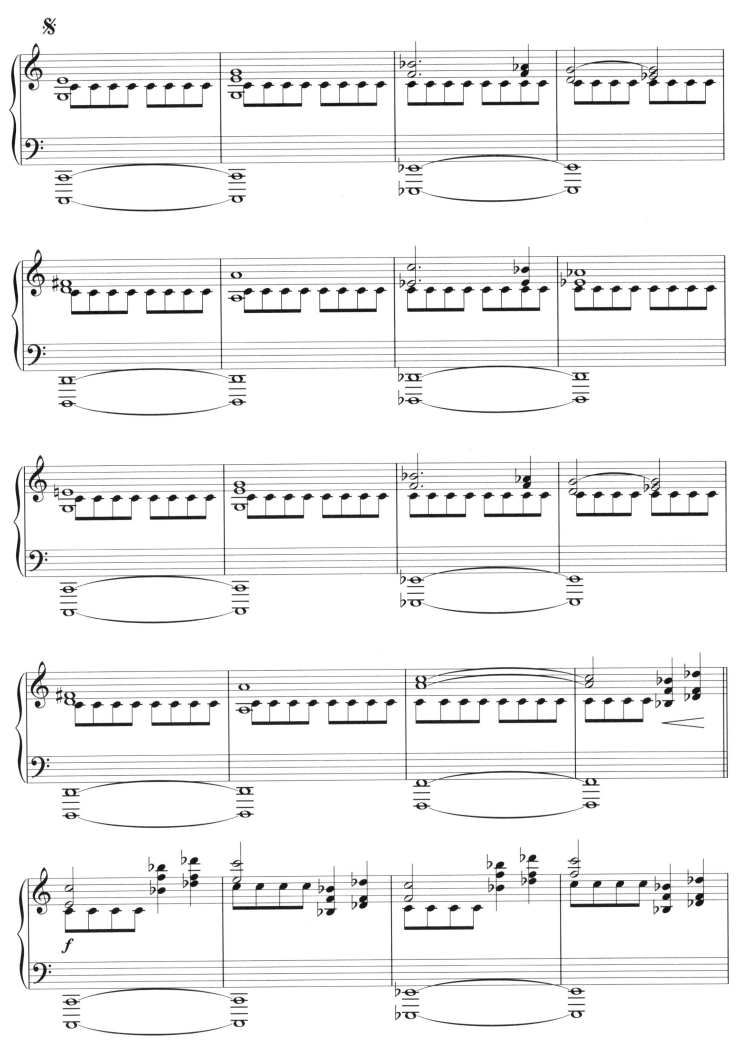

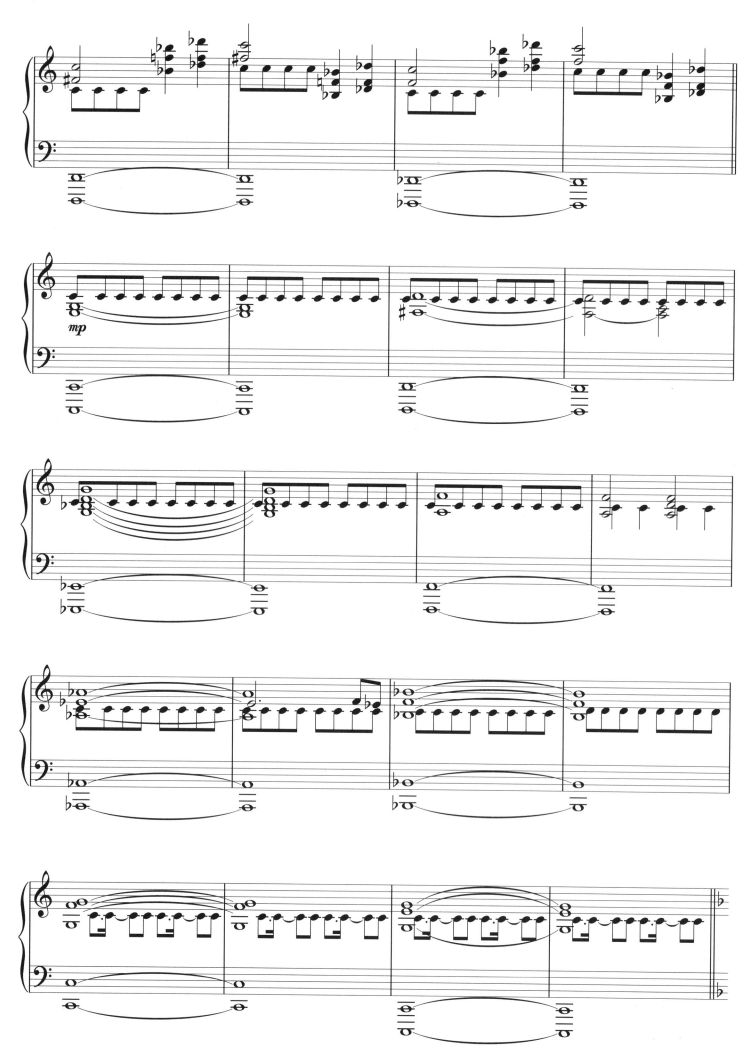

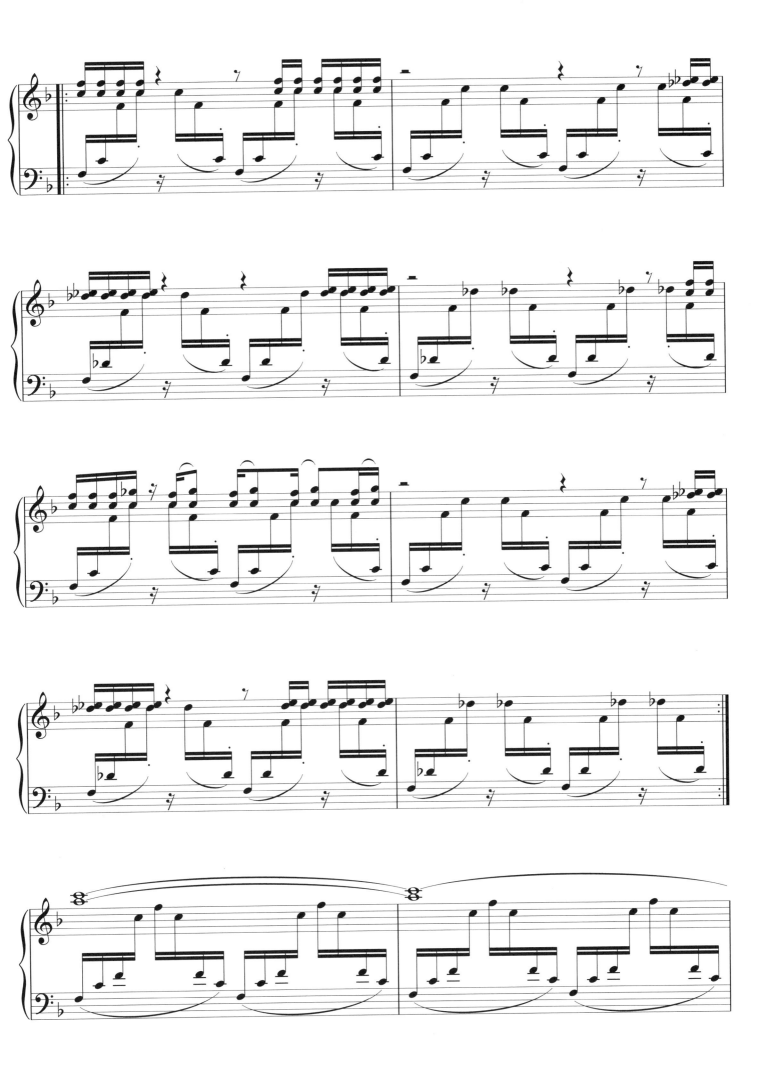

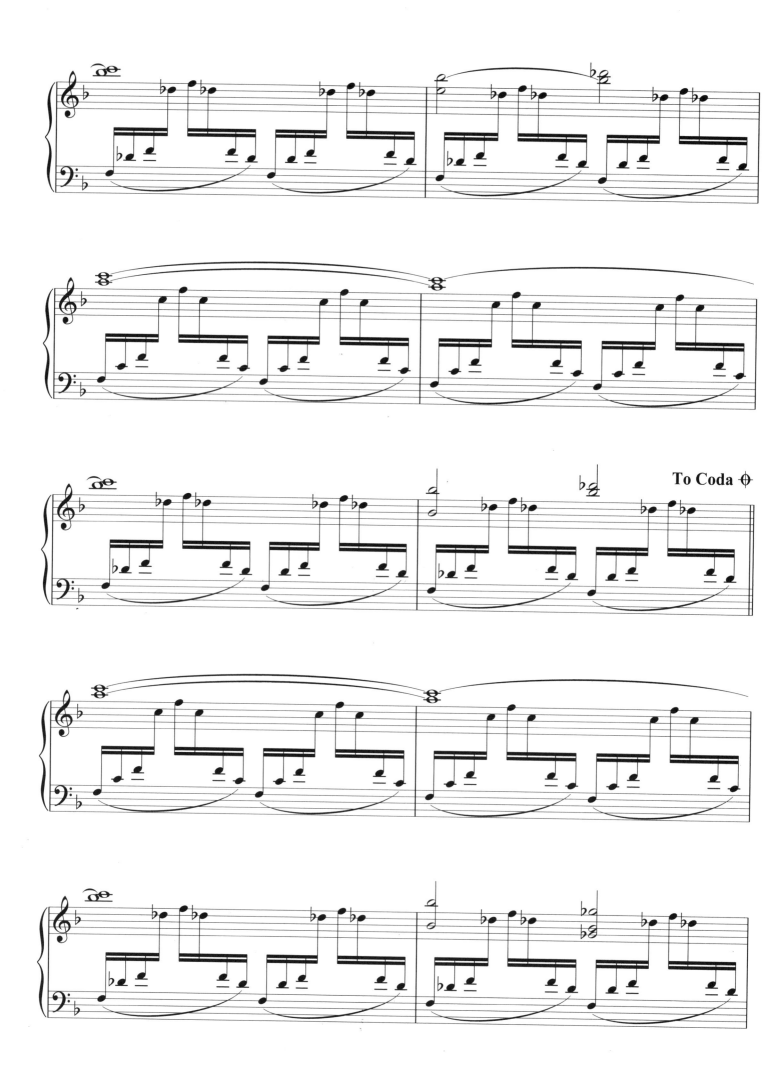

To Coda ✛

34

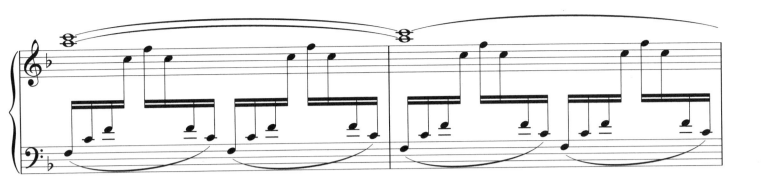

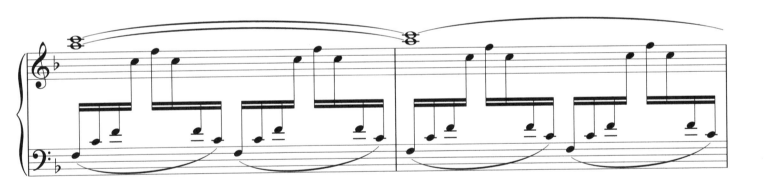

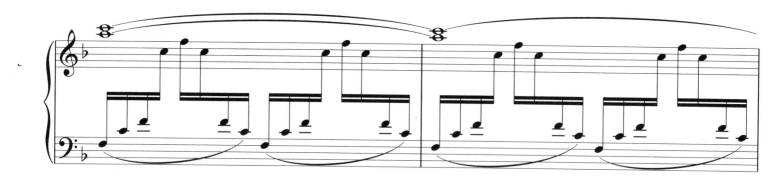

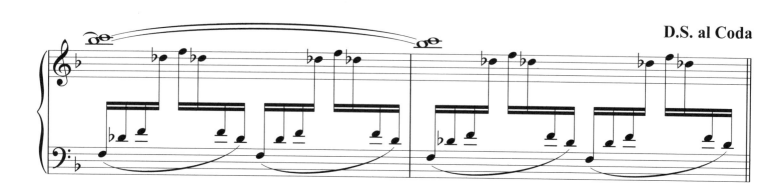

D.S. al Coda

⊕ Coda

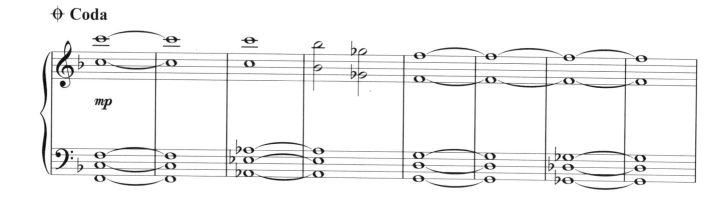

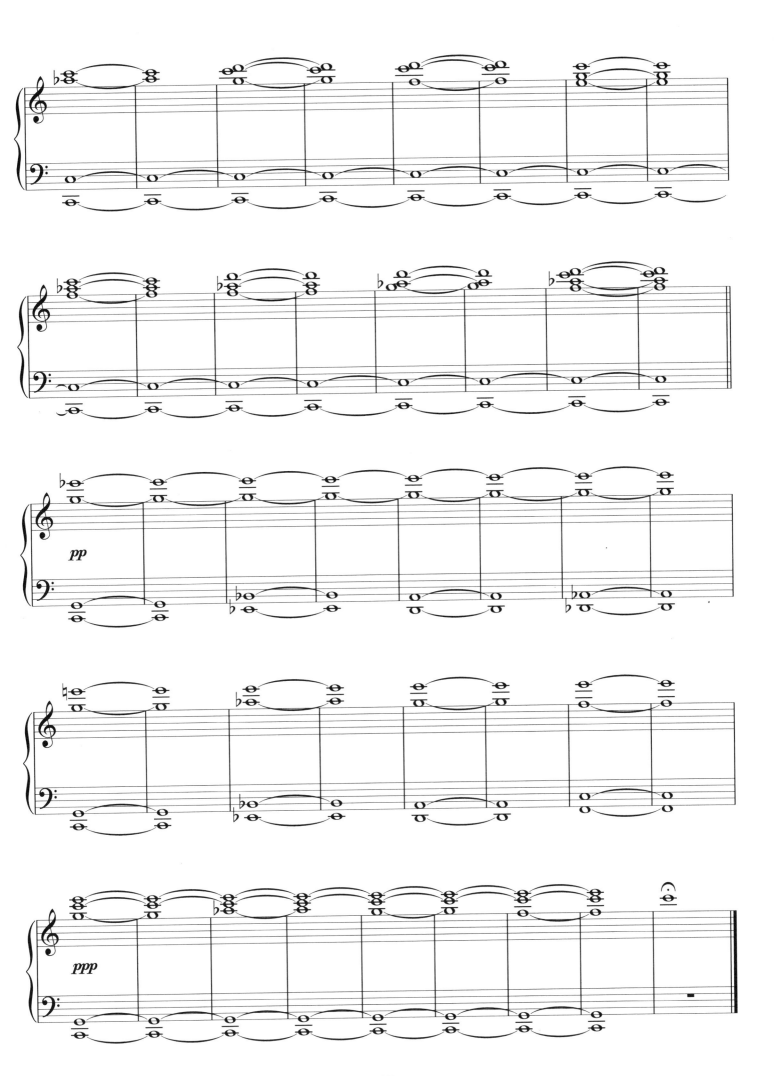

Fly A Kite/Reading The Letter

(FROM 'THE KITE RUNNER')

MUSIC BY ALBERTO IGLESIAS

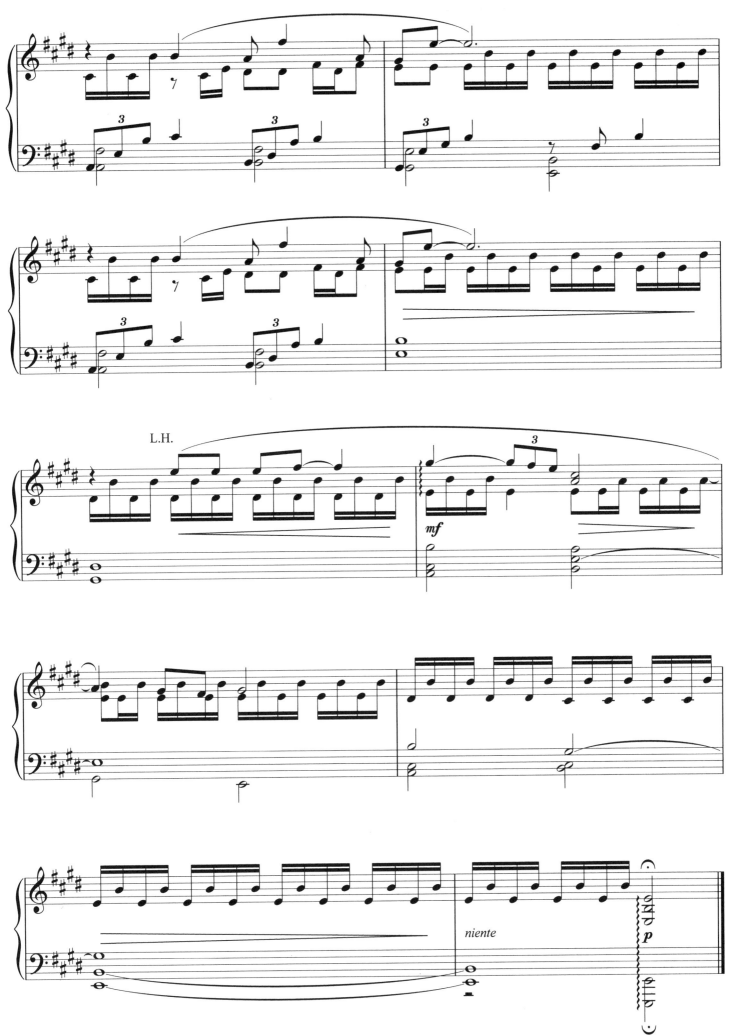

HARVEY'S LAST DAY
(FROM 'MILK')
MUSIC BY DANNY ELFMAN

Moderato

rit.

47

In The Library
(from 'Easy Virtue')
Music by Marius de Vries

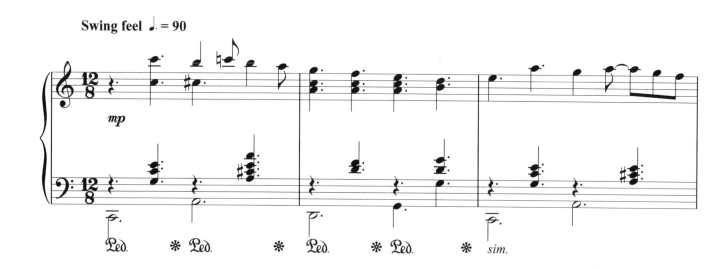

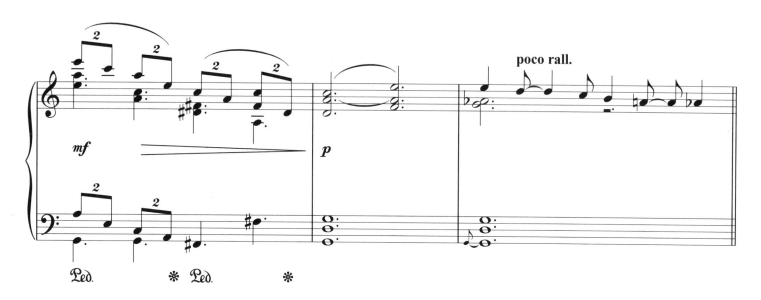

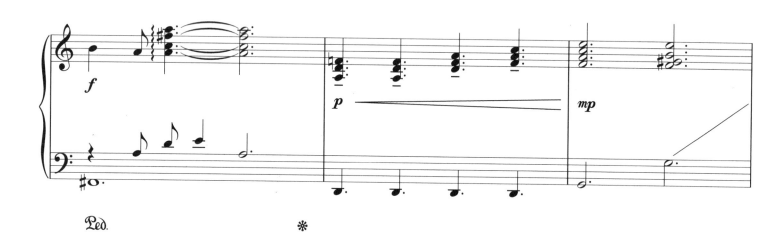

PROLOGUE/WALKING IN BRUGES/
RAY AT THE MIRROR
(FROM 'IN BRUGES')

MUSIC BY CARTER BURWELL

Latika's Theme
(FROM 'SLUMDOG MILLIONAIRE')
MUSIC BY A. R. RAHMAN

Moderately

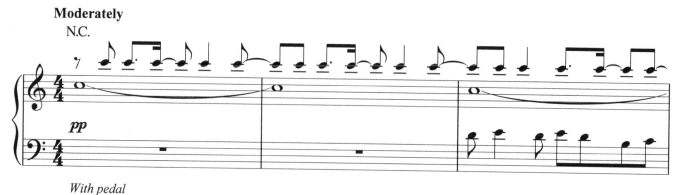

With pedal

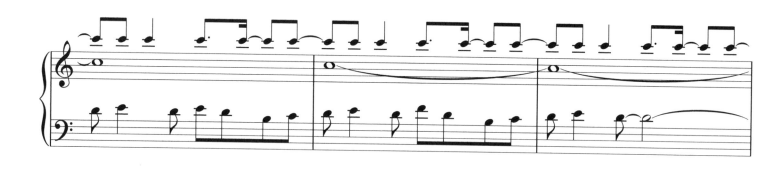

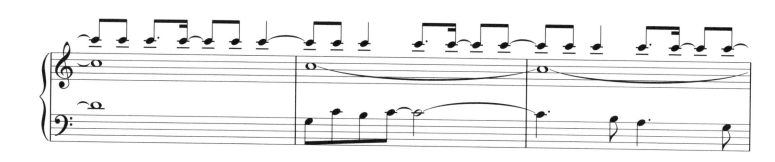

Minimal 4/Minimal 8

(FROM 'BLINDNESS')

MUSIC BY MARCO ANTÔNIO GUIMARÃES

MINIMAL 4

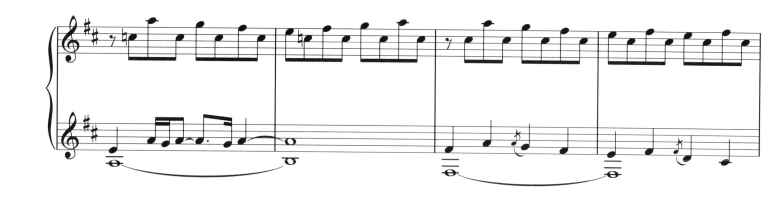

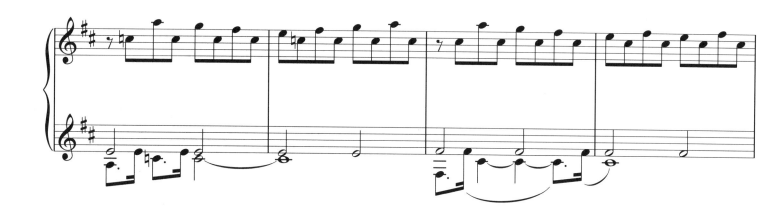

MINIMAL 8

Ped.   ✳

Ped.   ✳

Play 6 times

63

Sebastian
(FROM 'BRIDESHEAD REVISITED')
MUSIC BY ADRIAN JOHNSTON

65

66

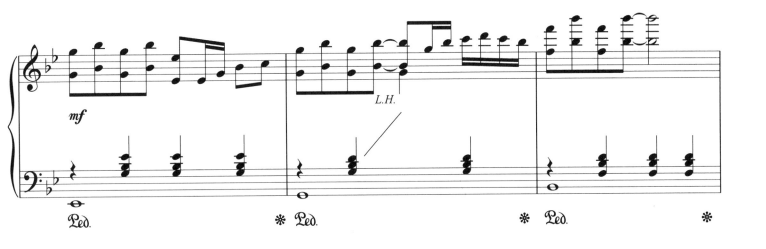

Salvation
(FROM 'TERMINATOR SALVATION')
MUSIC BY DANNY ELFMAN

TELSTAR
(FROM 'TELSTAR')
MUSIC BY JOE MEEK

75

That New Car Smell

(from 'Star Trek')

Music by Michael Giacchino

Then We Are Together
(from 'Let the Right One In')
Music by Johan Söderqvist

WALTER'S ETUDE NO. 1
(FROM 'THE VISITOR')
MUSIC BY JAN A. P. KACZMAREK

83

84

85

VICTORIA AND ALBERT
(FROM 'THE YOUNG VICTORIA')
MUSIC BY ILAN ESHKERI

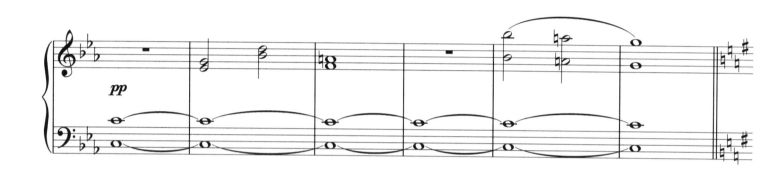

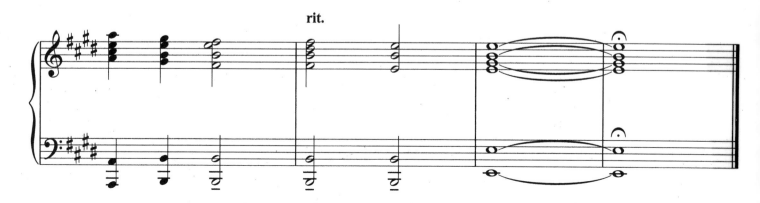